This book belongs to:_____

© This Edition
BABY'S FIRST BOOK CLUB®
Bristol, 19007 PA.

English text by Elna Greig and Kristina Blagojevitch.
© First Published by Éditions Nathan (Paris-France), 1995.
Original title: "Les Chiffres".
All rights reserved.
Printed in France.
by Pollina, 85400 Luçon - n° 71339

ISBN 1–881445–71–2

THE LITTLE RABBITS' BOOK OF

NUMBERS

Concept and text by Anaël Dana
Illustrations by Christel Desmoinaux

Baby's First Book Club®

ONE sweet little rabbit, one sunny day
goes joyfully into the garden to play.
His friend, the lamb
comes over too.
"Hello," says the rabbit.
"This daisy's for you!"

Find all the things there
is 1 of on this page.

Up in the attic is a great big box
full of old hats, books, shoes and socks.
TWO little rabbits
just love to explore.
"Look in here! I've found lots more!"

Find all the things there
are 2 of on this page.

THREE little rabbits
are having great fun.
They play in the park,
they hop and they run.
"I'll whizz down the slide
as fast as I can!
Luckily I'll land on
the nice, soft sand!"

Find all the things there
are 3 of on this page.

Frosty and white from his head to his toes,

the snowman is cold because

he's made of snow!

FOUR little rabbits made him today.

"Let's hope it stays chilly, or he'll melt away!"

Find all the things there are 4 of on this page.

FIVE little rabbits
enjoy their special tea.
"Happy Birthday, dear friend,"
they sing merrily.
One lucky rabbit is five years today.
He opens his presents –
hip, hip hurray!

Find all the things there
are 5 of on this page.

"Come on, everybody, the bus is here!"
Holiday time is the best time of year!
SIX little rabbits, big ones and small,
suitcases, bags – have they got them all?

**Find all the things there
are 6 of on this page.**

A day by the seaside
is such great fun,
splashing in the waves and lying in the sun.
Sand castles, ice creams, boat rides on the sea –
SEVEN little rabbits
are as happy as can be!

Find all the things there
are 7 of on this page.

EIGHT little rabbits
so keen and bright,
eager to learn how
to read and write.
Kind teacher Bunny
has just come in:
"Quiet, little rabbits!
Class will begin!"

Find all the things there
are 8 of on this page.

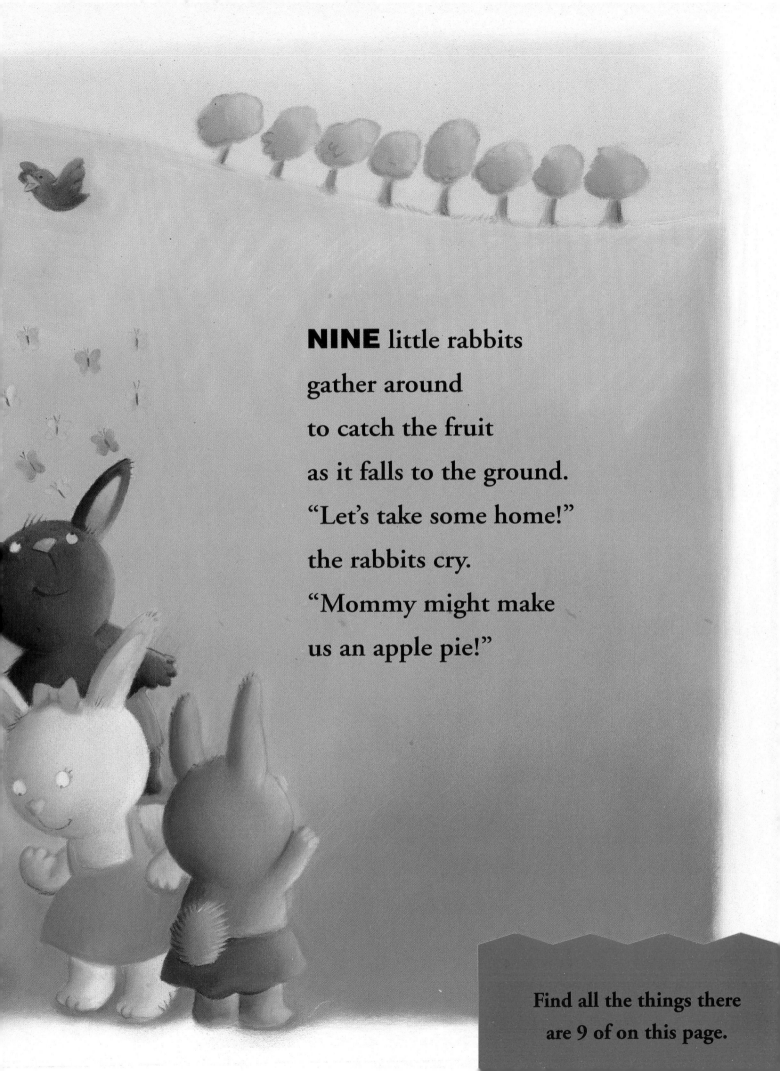

NINE little rabbits
gather around
to catch the fruit
as it falls to the ground.
"Let's take some home!"
the rabbits cry.
"Mommy might make
us an apple pie!"

Find all the things there
are 9 of on this page.

Frogs, ducks and fishes small
TEN rabbits can count them all.
"It's very late," one rabbit said.
"Good night, tadpoles,
it's time for bed."

24

Find all the things there
are 10 of on this page.

Counting rabbits

1   buys a loaf of bread

2   paint the walls blue

3   climb up a pole

4   knot their ties

5   have a nice bath

6   do their exercises

7   play the trumpet

8   run about

9   look at an egg

10   sleep in their bed

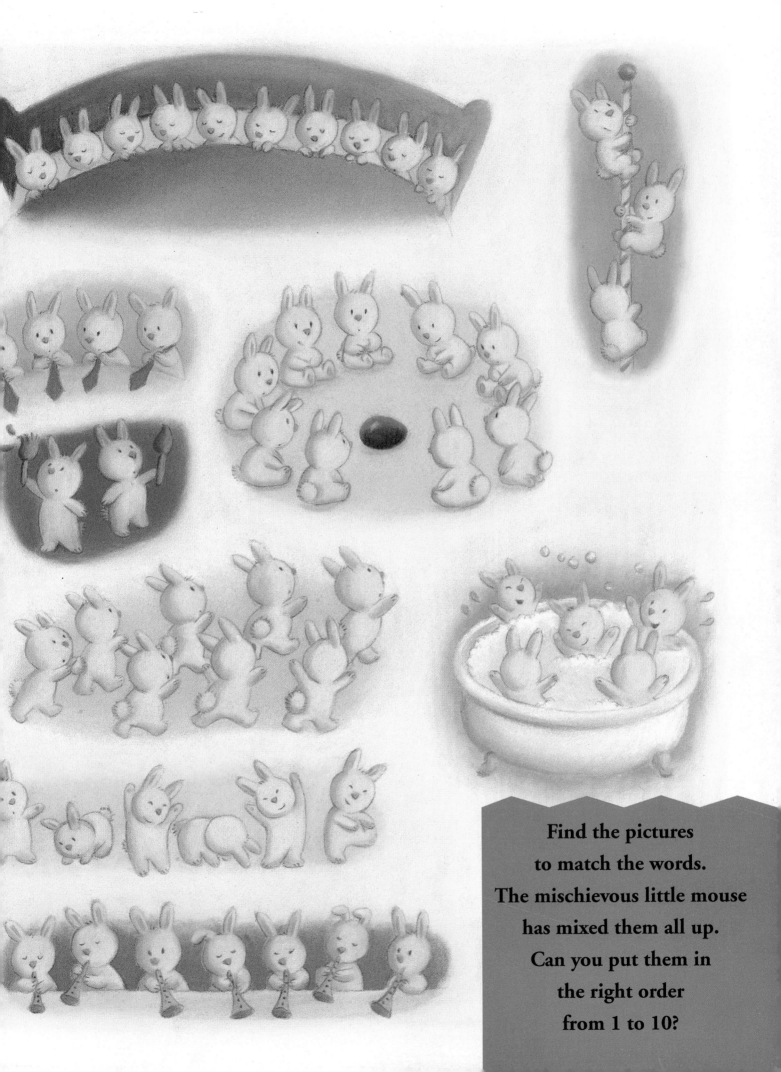

Find the pictures
to match the words.
The mischievous little mouse
has mixed them all up.
Can you put them in
the right order
from 1 to 10?

Hunting for Socks

It's easy to find shoes to wear

if you put them away in matching pairs.

The same goes for socks, it's a useful habit.

So, please can you help this poor little rabbit?

Help the rabbit
find the
matching socks.

Big Brother, Little Brother

Little baby rabbit and his big brother
are going to visit their dear Grandmother.
Look at their clothes, yes, look at them all.
Whose are the big things,
whose are the small?

Look at the rabbits.
Which is the smallest?
And which is the biggest?
Can you find which
things belong to
which rabbit?

Rabbit Cousins

Five rabbit cousins, all in a row,
dressed for a party, ready to go.
They're different sizes
and different ages.
Big cousin Ron is
too big for these pages!

Can you see cousin
Ron? Point at the
smallest cousin.
Is he the one with the
smallest bow tie?
Who is wearing
the biggest bow tie?
And who is wearing
the smallest?

The Rabbits' Treasures

The rabbits collect lots of things,
marbles, cars, stones, sticks and rings.
"How about swapping treasures with me?
One ring for two stones
– or maybe three!"

Count how many
there are of each thing.
Who has the most cars?
Who has the fewest rings?
Who has the most stones?
Who has the fewest marbles?
Who has the fewest sticks?

The Picnic

It's lovely to go for a nice, long walk,
then lie on the grass and eat and talk.
Sunshine and flowers
and plenty of food!
"How I love picnics!
The food tastes so good!"

Study the picture.
Are there as many
sheep as lambs?
Do the two rabbits
have the same number
of bread rolls each?
Are there just as many
plates as rabbits?
Are there just as many
apples as rabbits?

The Turtle Race

The yearly turtle race is on.
The fastest turtle finally won.
The track was hard,
they did their best.
Now they deserve
a nice, long rest.

FINISH

START

Can you count how
many turtles there
are in the red team?
And in the yellow team?
How many turtles
are there all together?
Look at the turtle
who is going to win.
How many lettuces
will he win as a prize?

The Collectors

Little rabbit and his big brother
have lots of cards to show each other.
Animal pictures to collect and share —
fish in the sea, butterflies in the air.

Look at the picture
cards on the wall.
How many butterflies
can you see?
How many fish?
Look at the cards
on the floor.
How many cards
will each rabbit get?
How many cards
are there all together
in the room?

The Rabbit Race

The rules of the game:
You need one counter for each player
and a die. Each player chooses his track
and puts his counter in the start area.
Take turns at throwing the die and
move the counter forward according
to the number on the die.
The first to reach the finish
is the winner.

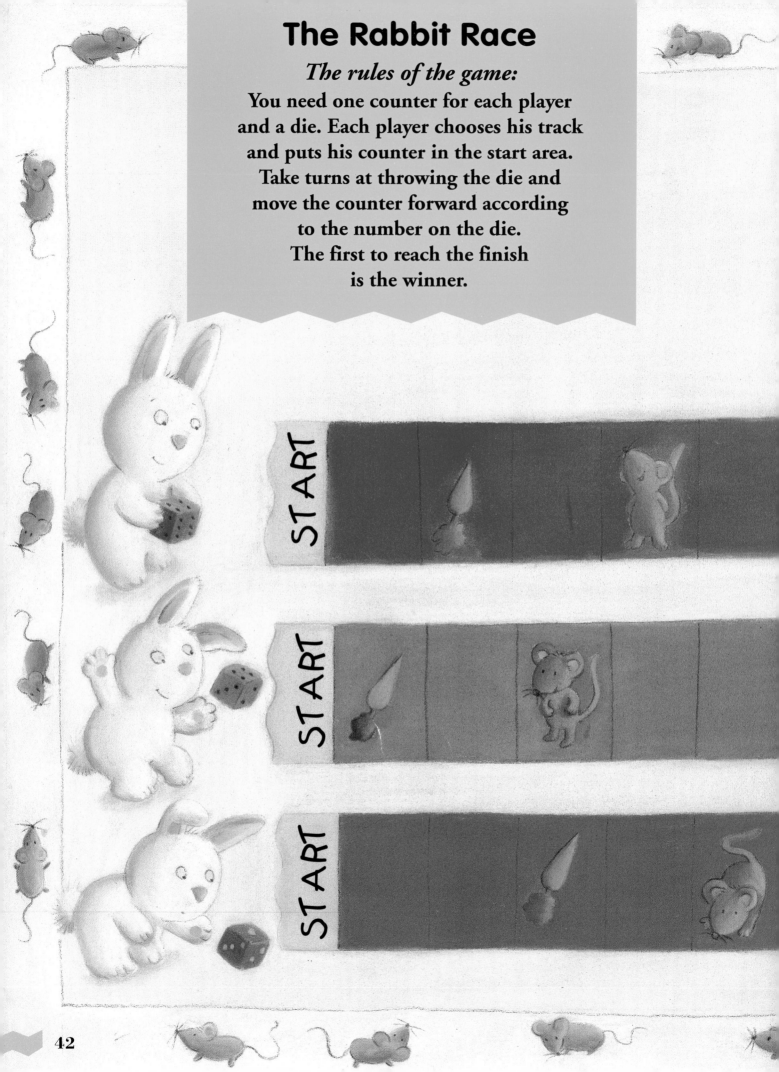

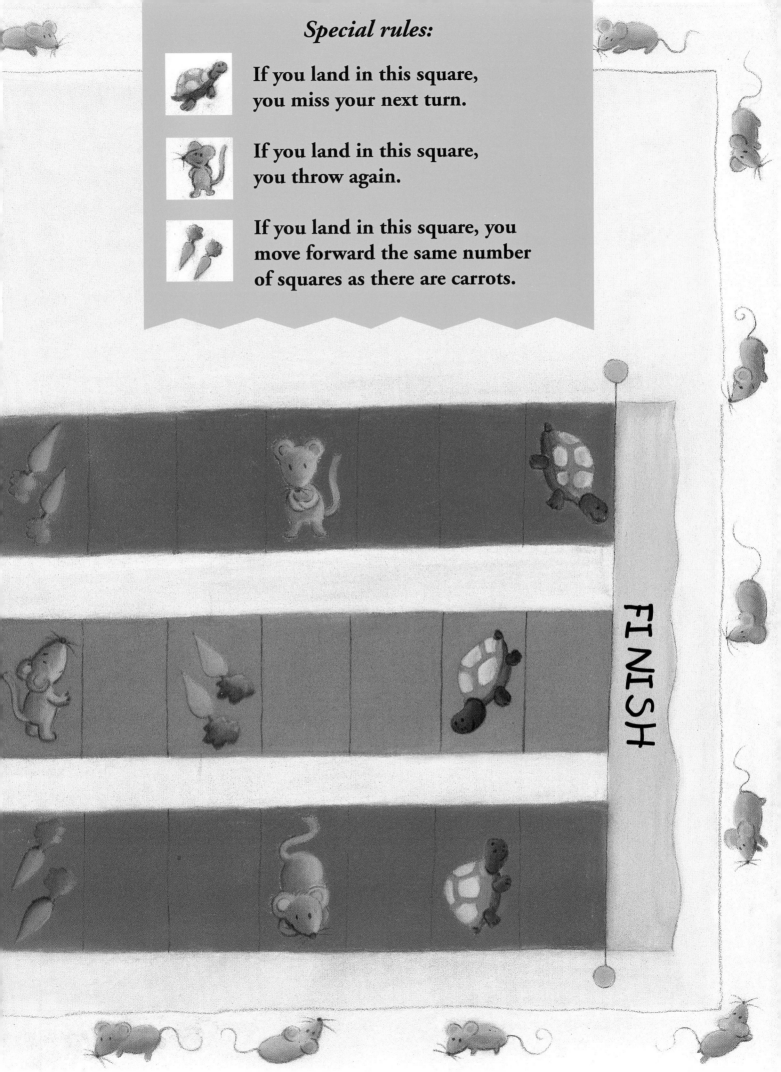

Special rules:

If you land in this square, you miss your next turn.

If you land in this square, you throw again.

If you land in this square, you move forward the same number of squares as there are carrots.

FINISH

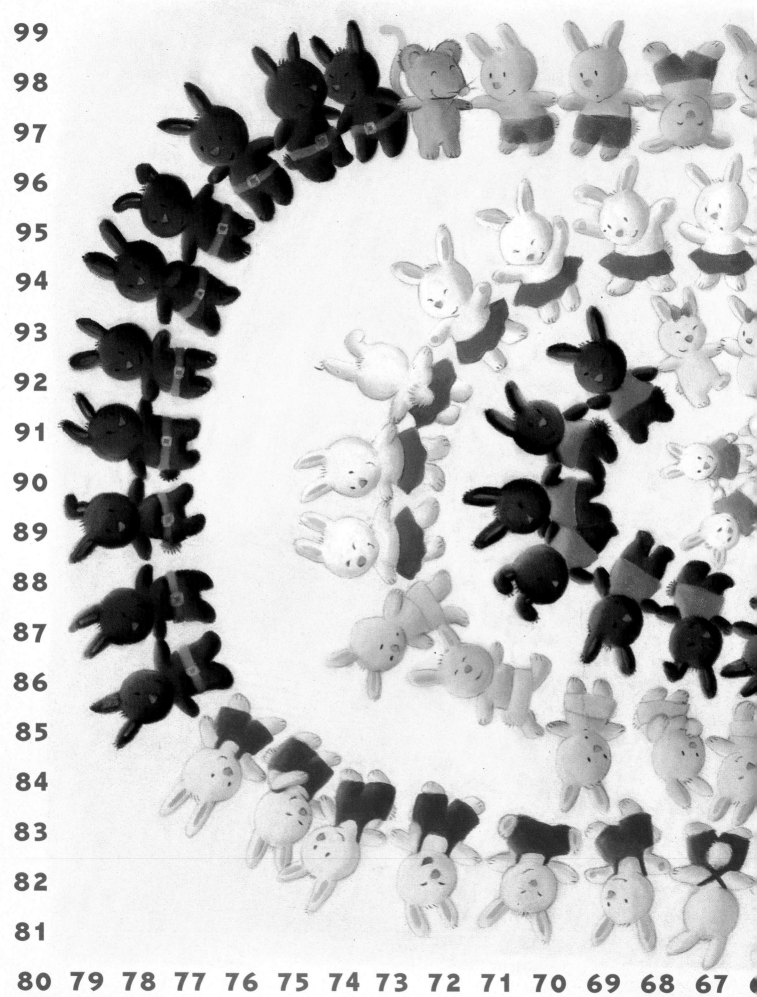

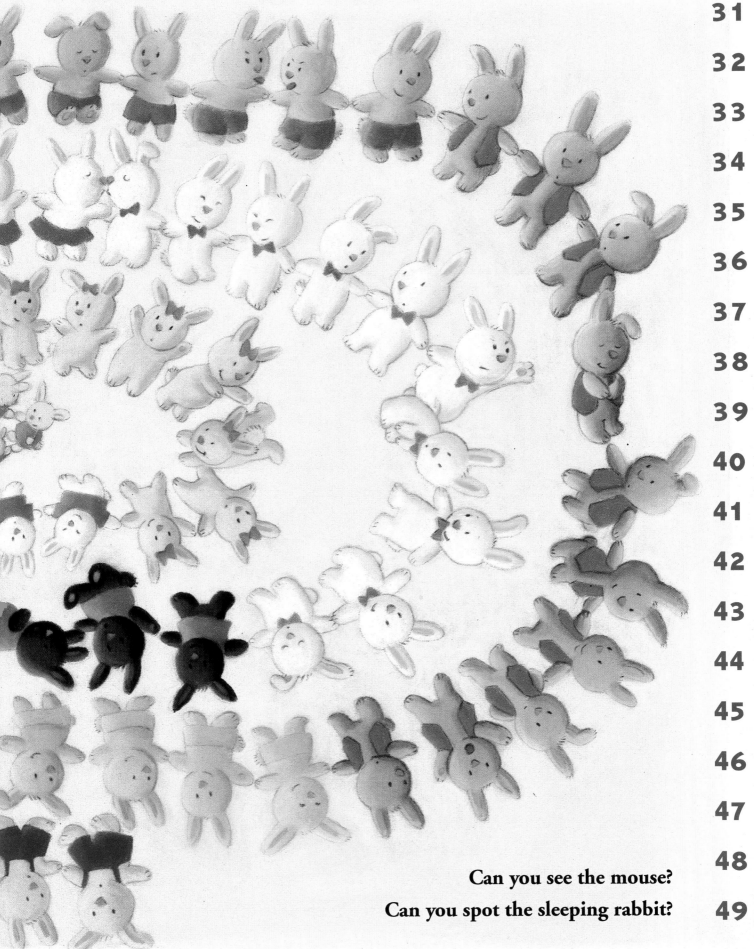

Can you see the mouse?
Can you spot the sleeping rabbit?

1

2

5

8

9